This Book of Poems Belongs to:

ⓐ a creative genius

ⓑ a literary icon

ⓒ me (aka _____)

YOU'RE A POET, AND DON'T KNOW IT.

Perhaps you don't have

ⓐ time to craft a personalized poetic missive

ⓑ the ability to express yourself in words

ⓒ a black turtleneck and beret

And you wish you had

ⓐ a degree in English literature

ⓑ your own personal Cyrano de Bergerac

ⓒ human emotions because you're a robot

Relax! Help is here!
Enter Instant Poetry.

At last, there's a place for you to

ⓐ describe your intense love of nature's beauty

ⓑ bemoan the state of affairs in #contemporary life

ⓒ let your inner goth out

Now you can enjoy

ⓐ the miracle of choosing checkboxes

ⓑ the ease of using someone else's words

ⓒ sneakily passing these poems off as your own

And craft just the right sentiment to express your feelings when you are

ⓐ frisky

ⓑ sentimental

ⓒ uninspired

And all you have to do is

ⓐ read the options carefully and choose your favorite

ⓑ skim the options quickly and make an impulsive choice

ⓒ close your eyes and point your finger somewhere on the page

Simply

ⓐ write your choice in the provided space

ⓑ recopy your poem to share it in a letter, blog, email, or school assignment

ⓒ hire a skywriter to emblazon it across the skyline

Congratulations!
You're about to become

ⓐ a tortured artist

ⓑ the Shakespeare of our time

ⓒ poet laureate of your living room

NOW, GO FORTH, AND WRITE!

LINE 1

ⓐ leaves wafting down
ⓑ light dusts streets gold
ⓒ thunders in quick

LINE 2

ⓐ I Google old lovers
ⓑ I eat cake in the dark
ⓒ crabs scuttle in my pants

LINE 3

ⓐ Who cooked up all
ⓑ What strange waltz is
ⓒ How'd it come to

Fall _____
1

as _____.
2

_____ this?
3

COUPLET

LINE 1
ⓐ air hides nature's womb
ⓑ breath of floral bloom
ⓒ dusk halts pollen plume

LINE 2
ⓐ Tim Burton in the gloom
ⓑ a bride without a groom
ⓒ heroes fighting Dr. Doom

A foggy _____,
1

Found by _____.
2

RHYMED VERSE

LINE 1
ⓐ local greens and candied yams
ⓑ brioche bites and artisan jam
ⓒ PBR tallboy in a can

LINE 2
ⓐ quip about a senator's affair
ⓑ link I just shared
ⓒ yoga pose held in midair

LINE 3
ⓐ make me famous on Instagram
ⓑ get likes from friends and fam
ⓒ attract some major brands

LINE 4
ⓐ my Twitter notifications bare
ⓑ no doubt that no one cares
ⓒ me stranded online but nowhere

LINE 5
ⓐ Snapchat story of a sexy nerd
ⓑ meme with "ermahgerd"
ⓒ post with trending words

LINE 6
ⓐ go viral by tonight
ⓑ make me look super bright
ⓒ boost my clicks to the heights

LINE 7
ⓐ fall behind the herd
ⓑ step in a social turd
ⓒ fail to get anyone stirred

LINE 8
ⓐ get swiped left instead of right
ⓑ is my selfie in bad light
ⓒ should I boost my post tonight

If my _____
1

or my _____
2

doesn't _____
3

and leaves _____,
4

if my _____
5

won't _____,
6

did I _____
7

or _____?
8

LIMERICK

LINE 1
ⓐ a man from Sioux City
ⓑ a hipster groomed pretty
ⓒ a thug, sweet and gritty

LINE 2
ⓐ thought of himself as quite witty
ⓑ wanted not romance but pity
ⓒ admired old G. Gordon Liddy

LINE 3
ⓐ banter was gruff
ⓑ game was all bluff
ⓒ hands were in cuffs

LINE 4
ⓐ cigars he did puff
ⓑ his charm not enough
ⓒ he spoke lots of guff

LINE 5
ⓐ ex-wives called him shitty
ⓑ manhood was itty bitty
ⓒ lone friend was a kitty

There once was _____
1

who _____.
2

But his _____
3

and _____.
4

No surprise his _____.
5

#CONTEMPORARY

LINE 1
(a) whiteboard of my soul
(b) sticky note affixed to my cubicle
(c) pie chart on slide 36 of the marketing PowerPoint

LINE 2
(a) Xeroxed our asses
(b) told Jeannine in accounting that Monday was a holiday
(c) took incriminating photos at the office party

LINE 3
(a) someone brings donuts
(b) there's someone cute in the office to flirt with
(c) you're playing Words with Friends in the bathroom

LINE 4
(a) on Friday afternoons
(b) when it's just you and the boss in the elevator
(c) when the IT guy corners you by the watercooler

LINE 5
(a) an overturned recycling bin
(b) bullet points in the wind
(c) layoffs in the spring

LINE 6
(a) a long holiday break
(b) comprehensive KPIs tied to individual VAR channels
(c) ergonomic anything

LINE 7
(a) powerful synergy
(b) visionary disruption
(c) beneficial rightsizing

LINE 8
(a) our corporate overlords
(b) questionable acquisition targets
(c) the long bathroom line at a sales conference

LINE 9
(a) social media influencer
(b) highly paid consultant
(c) guy carried out on a stretcher

LINE 10
(a) We're all in this together
(b) See you on Saturday
(c) Yes, but will it scale?

"I Sing the Modern Selectric"

Imprinted on the _____
                                        1

_____

is the memory of the time we _____
                                          2

_____.

Time! How swiftly it flies when _____
                                          3

_____

and how slowly it drags _____
                                        4

_____.

Action items unfold like _____.
                                        5

Blessed art those who receive _____
                                          6

_____.

Comrades! Awake to the _____
                                        7

of _____.
                                        8

For, as the _____ declared,
                                        9

"_____!"
                                        10

LINE 1

ⓐ just here for the free booze
ⓑ an actor/comedian/percussionist/waiter
ⓒ not myself today

LINE 2

ⓐ thirsty
ⓑ over this
ⓒ faking it

I'm _____
1

_____! Who are you?

Are you _____ too?
2

LINE 1
ⓐ on my ass
ⓑ eating ham
ⓒ hamster-like

LINE 2
ⓐ the universe
ⓑ it all for naught
ⓒ potato chips

LINE 3
ⓐ a bite, crunch
ⓑ it like hmmm
ⓒ a long whiz, amen

I sat _____,
                  1

pondering _____.
                  2

I took _____.
                  3

SURREALIST

LINE 1
(a) planets
(b) insects
(c) stockbrokers

(a) exploding
(b) feeding
(c) high-fiving

LINE 2
(a) the death star
(b) nobody's business
(c) yesterday's breakfast burrito

LINE 3
(a) lotus-eater
(b) puppet master
(c) surrealist poet

LINE 4
(a) terribly cozy
(b) ironically ironic
(c) totally out of ideas

LINE 5
(a) walk jauntily
(b) wield a machete to hack my way
(c) ignore those jerks from high school

LINE 6
(a) fruit trees in spring
(b) lunch crowd at Quiznos
(c) stoners at a Phish concert

LINE 7
(a) last
(b) the billions and billions of stars
(c) something surreal TBD

LINE 8
(a) where grandma fell last year
(b) a poor substitute for an elevator
(c) very French

(a) Huzzah
(b) OMG
(c) Gah

LINE 9
(a) shouted so surprisingly loud that
   I peed a little, too
(b) somehow recalled from hanging
   out in summer camp
(c) rapped smooth and convincingly

LINE 10
(a) meself, into my soup
(b) my English composition teacher
(c) the adoring crowd

LINE 11
(a) 'tis sweet sorrow
(b) completes my MFA
(c) at last

"Clamoring Muffin Tape Measures!"

The _____ are _____
         1   1

like _____.
              2

My dear _____,
                  3

how _____ you are!
              4

I _____
      5

amidst the _____.
                  6

I look up at _____.
                    7

The staircase is _____,
                        8

" _____!"
        8

I _____
    9

_____

"How strange!" cried _____,
                              10

to finish a poem _____.
                        11

LINE 1

ⓐ Please stop looking at the clock

ⓑ Tell a secret, I won't squawk

ⓒ Stinky, smelly athletic sock

Hickory dickory dock,

_____.

MODERN GOTHIC

LINE 1
ⓐ Black Day, Black Night
ⓑ You Know Who
ⓒ Mom & Dad

LINE 2
ⓐ cast my heart into darkness
ⓑ elected to torment me so sweetly
ⓒ been so totally totally lame

LINE 3
ⓐ the exquisite pain of crying into my spicy vegan ramen
ⓑ that day I lost the keys to the Prius
ⓒ my parents not understanding me

LINE 4
ⓐ like, so confusing!
ⓑ my middle name
ⓒ totally my parents' middle names

LINE 5
ⓐ of death
ⓑ I would never do in public
ⓒ my parents made me practice as a kid

LINE 6
ⓐ now upon us
ⓑ the time to awaken
ⓒ the witching hour (duh!!)

LINE 7
ⓐ shadow figure haunting my dreams
ⓑ circles under your eyes
ⓒ nemesis, haha! We meet again!

LINE 8
ⓐ have a dark need
ⓑ am about
ⓒ harbor an uncontrollable kink

LINE 9
ⓐ drink
ⓑ suck on
ⓒ steal

ⓐ blood
ⓑ toes
ⓒ soul and/or TV

LINE 10
ⓐ a romantic, undead aristocrat
ⓑ wearing a lot of pancake makeup
ⓒ legally not permitted to go more than 1,000 yards from my house

Dear _____ 1 _____:

Why have you _____ 2 _____?

This feels like _____ 3 _____

_____.

Confusion is _____ 4 _____.

Truly, this is the dance _____ 5 _____

_____.

Midnight is _____ 6 _____.

I see the dark _____ 7 _____.

Yes! I _____ 8 _____

to _____ 9 _____ your _____ 9 _____.

Fear me, for I am _____ 10 _____

_____!

LINE 1
ⓐ like a shot
ⓑ out of tears
ⓒ in undies

LINE 2
ⓐ this is amazeballs
ⓑ with risk comes reward
ⓒ of my life's meaning

LINE 3
ⓐ You go, girl!!
ⓑ Intriguing
ⓒ Wow, that's odd

I ran _____,
1

thinking _____.
2

They said, "_____!"
3

PASTORAL

LINE 1
ⓐ fine young shepherds
ⓑ star-crossed lovers
ⓒ freelance lyre tuners

ⓐ bucolic countryside
ⓑ sylvan meadow
ⓒ Forest Glen Community Estates™

LINE 2
ⓐ Hark!
ⓑ What ho!
ⓒ Thou art that which stirs in me

ⓐ whilst forking hay
ⓑ with great ardor
ⓒ pastorally

LINE 3
ⓐ sneezewort
ⓑ toadflax
ⓒ sheepdip

ⓐ the country air
ⓑ yon pigsty
ⓒ yon faerie ring

LINE 4
ⓐ Checkered is the cornfield of fall
ⓑ The beauty of spring
ⓒ Winter is coming

LINE 5
ⓐ yon castle
ⓑ thy cowshed
ⓒ my place

➤ Two _____ met in the
                              1

_____.
                              1

"_____," one proffered,
                              2

_____.
                              2

"How the _____ perfumes
                              3

_____!"
                              3

"Aye," declaimed the other. "_____
                              4

_____!"

And thusly, for a night, with both gods and men lured by

the song of sirens to abandon all cares and labours, the

first cried out to the second: "Meet me at _____
                                                    5

_____!"

ODE

LINE 1
ⓐ weep tonight, forever ruined
ⓑ are flowers, very expensive, typically red
ⓒ ...oh, never mind, you up?

LINE 2
ⓐ they mock my very existence
ⓑ the salesperson tells me so
ⓒ ...uh, hey. whattup?

LINE 3
ⓐ are swallowed by the dark night
ⓑ are quite fascinating if you under-stand physics
ⓒ better look out, cause here I come, baybee!!

LINE 4
ⓐ I took too many anxiety meds
ⓑ believe it or not, I'm still a virgin
ⓒ and so does my crotch

LINE 5
ⓐ *Why did you leave*
ⓑ *What would Wookies having sex sound like*
ⓒ *wanna hookup*

LINE 6
ⓐ therapist
ⓑ D&D Grandmaster
ⓒ doctor

LINE 7
ⓐ try and forget you
ⓑ level up on magic love potions
ⓒ take more vitamin U

LINE 8
ⓐ my life has lost its meaning
ⓑ the earth will continue spinning, however less enjoyable
ⓒ ima hit the #gym #goalz

 **"Ode to Roses...and U"**

Roses _____ .
                                    1

This I know, for _____ .
                                    2

The stars above _____ .
                                    3

My heart burns with a secret: _____
                                    4

_____ .

It has but one question for you: _____
                                    5

_____ ?

I called my _____ , who told me to
                                    6

_____ .
                                    7

For without you, my beloved, _____
                                    8

_____ .

LINE 1
ⓐ a pisser
ⓑ a #blessing
ⓒ yesterday

LINE 2
ⓐ like super deep
ⓑ drunk, happy, sad
ⓒ slugging my boss

LINE 3
ⓐ steal my thunder
ⓑ harsh my mellow
ⓒ post this (or else)

Today's _____.
1

OK, I'm _____.
2

Don't _____.
3

FREE VERSE

LINE 1
ⓐ splits the horizon
ⓑ ripples in the heat
ⓒ weighs down the Earth

LINE 2
ⓐ black Fruit Roll-Up™
ⓑ dancing tar pit
ⓒ rope of asphalt

LINE 3
ⓐ fingers sweat
ⓑ tires howl
ⓒ coffee goes cold

LINE 4
ⓐ eyes fight the sun
ⓑ leg starts to cramp
ⓒ Debbie Gibson playlist ends

LINE 5
ⓐ tarantula waits
ⓑ hobo gestures
ⓒ stranger who looks like my
   ex pauses

LINE 6
ⓐ weakest prey to pass
ⓑ dusk's dark embrace
ⓒ ayahuasca to kick in

LINE 7
ⓐ two hundred more miles to Reno
ⓑ dotted yellow lines between me
   and the border
ⓒ cruelty can keep me from the city

LINE 8
ⓐ network at the insurance sales
   convention
ⓑ have a smoke and a beignet
ⓒ get myself a really good hat

The road _____
                          1

like a _____
                          2

while my _____
                          3

and my _____.
                          4

Ahead a _____
                          5

for the _____.
                          6

Only _____
                          7

where I'll _____.
                          8

ODE

LINE 1
ⓐ heart
ⓑ passion
ⓒ your booty

LINE 2
ⓐ hand
ⓑ eyes
ⓒ tongue

LINE 3
ⓐ undress
ⓑ offer up
ⓒ tie up

LINE 4
ⓐ soul
ⓑ life
ⓒ muffin top

LINE 5
ⓐ devour
ⓑ lick
ⓒ dry hump

LINE 6
ⓐ fever
ⓑ thirst
ⓒ yearning

LINE 7
ⓐ haunt you
ⓑ climax prematurely
ⓒ try to ignore the dog sniffing my underwear on the floor

"Ode to a One-Night Stand"

'Tis _____
₁

That guides my _____
₂

As I _____
₃

My _____
₄

For you to _____.
₅

With this _____
₆

I shall _____
₇

_____.

LINE 1

ⓐ Unless they're dead and thick with mold

ⓑ I think that's true, or so I'm told

ⓒ There's more to call when you're paroled

Make new friends but keep the old.

1

#CONTEMPORARY

LINE 1
ⓐ Kardashian, my Kardashian
ⓑ solitude, for the internet is down
ⓒ days of youth and Coachella

LINE 2
ⓐ tweets have gone un-re-tweeted
ⓑ friend can't get us in the club
ⓒ yoga instructor now does spin

LINE 3
ⓐ selfie sticks
ⓑ downward dogs
ⓒ gourmet food trucks

LINE 4
ⓐ that vape store my friend told
   me about
ⓑ that dispensary my cousin told
   me about
ⓒ something to wear to Burning Man

LINE 5
ⓐ looked up Kanye lyrics
ⓑ ordered the tofu version
ⓒ switched to Sprint

LINE 6
ⓐ Who knows what Kanye's talking
   about anyway
ⓑ Who still checks in on Foursquare
ⓒ Who has not seen my Snapchat
   pretty filter

LINE 7
ⓐ All your base are belong to us
ⓑ Needs more cowbell
ⓒ #soblessed

O, _____!
1

My _____.
2

I wandered through the forest of _____
3

_____

looking, searching in vain for _____
4

_____.

In my desperation, I _____.
5

Universe, I ask you: _____
6

_____?

Lo! For it is written in the stars: _____
7

_____.

IN THE STYLE OF E. E. CUMMINGS

LINE 1
ⓐ nap time
ⓑ happy hour
ⓒ spring break

LINE 2
ⓐ pie-eyed
ⓑ peg-legged
ⓒ pervy

LINE 3
ⓐ hums
ⓑ blows
ⓒ frightens clowns

LINE 4
ⓐ sad
ⓑ lucky
ⓒ like a hillbilly drunk

it's

_____
1

and

    the

       _____
           2

balloonMan   _____
               3

_____
4

and

wee

LINE 1

ⓐ say, "Ha!"
ⓑ taunt me
ⓒ taste sad

LINE 2

ⓐ crushed on the sidewalk
ⓑ when you've been ghosted
ⓒ like a sweet love lost

LINE 3

ⓐ dance-off you botched
ⓑ fourth drink you had
ⓒ goatee you grew

Candy hearts _____
                        1

_____ thanks to
                        2

that _____.
                        3

LINE 1
ⓐ date lacks common sense
ⓑ talk is dull and dense
ⓒ scent is too intense

Courtly love is on the fence

When one's _____.
1

FREE VERSE

LINE 1
ⓐ the way a fly regards a frog
ⓑ with a strange feeling in his loins
ⓒ as the type of person who'd eventually
need a restraining order

LINE 2
ⓐ with unjustified contempt
ⓑ through two holes cut out of
a newspaper
ⓒ as a slob, but an employed slob

LINE 3
ⓐ was extremely awkward
ⓑ felt lumpy
ⓒ existed in someone else's house

LINE 4
ⓐ even met
ⓑ knew what to have for dinner
ⓒ discussed religion or politics

He regarded her _____
                                          1
_____,

and she viewed him _____
                                          2
_____.

The bed they shared _____,
                                          3
and they never _____.
                                  4

LINE 1

ⓐ happen to see me act mean
ⓑ rock out to good bands like Queen
ⓒ own any shorts made of jean

LINE 2

ⓐ go get some codeine
ⓑ dance like a sardine
ⓒ self-publish a 'zine

If you _____,

1

It's best to _____.

2

LINE 1

ⓐ Loved sarcastic commentary
ⓑ Never shaved, thus quite hairy
ⓒ Never lacked an adversary

Mary, Mary, quite contrary,

_____ .

1

BEAT

LINE 1
ⓐ Nope, nope, nope
ⓑ Dig it
ⓒ Turn on, tune in, drop out

LINE 2
ⓐ are doomed
ⓑ think with their cell phones
ⓒ abide

LINE 3
ⓐ moronic
ⓑ quixotic
ⓒ brilliant

ⓐ slovenly
ⓑ desperate
ⓒ libidinous

LINE 4
ⓐ are doomed
ⓑ think with their cell phones
ⓒ abide

LINE 5
ⓐ fed lies like soup from an
   endless tureen
ⓑ led like lambs to the
   corporate slaughter
ⓒ forever forced to miss
   The Grateful Dead

LINE 6
ⓐ a drum circle circles round to beat
   beat beat
ⓑ the dream catcher turns into a sea
   of spiders
ⓒ the audience snaps fingers in praise

LINE 7
ⓐ at the irony of life
ⓑ at the sad idealism of classes
ⓒ in solidarity with the bourgeois

LINE 8
ⓐ Nope, nope, nope
ⓑ Dig it
ⓒ Turn on, tune in, drop out

The people? _____ .
1

The people _____ .
2

The _____ and _____
3   3

people _____ .
4

They will be _____

_____ ,

and when they least expect it _____
6

_____ .

The great ones smile _____ .
7

The people? _____ .
8

HAIKU

LINE 1
ⓐ destiny?
ⓑ from the edge
ⓒ you hot mess

LINE 2
ⓐ a truckload of joy
ⓑ a boatload of cash
ⓒ a shitload of ham

LINE 3
ⓐ life and stuff
ⓑ I'm hangry
ⓒ I said so

Hello, _____1_____!

Bring me _____2_____.

Because _____3_____.

MODERN GOTHIC

LINE 1
ⓐ train is ready to depart
ⓑ in my blood hits my heart
ⓒ cloud breaks apart

LINE 2
ⓐ cares to see
ⓑ knows the creed
ⓒ slows their speed

LINE 3
ⓐ shadows stretch beyond
   our homes
ⓑ night bird screeches all alone
ⓒ people move through days
   like drones

LINE 4
ⓐ plants its seed
ⓑ waits for me
ⓒ makes us bleed

The chemical _____ .
                                    1

But no one _____ .
                                    2

When _____ ,
                          3

the darkness _____ .
                                    4

LINE 1

ⓐ She had to size up when her kids all grew
ⓑ Resentful because it was missing a loo
ⓒ I cannot believe you think that is true

There was an old woman who lived in a shoe.

_____.
1

FREE VERSE

LINE 1
(a) device keeps me connected to
(b) Tinder profile gets me in with
(c) followers update me on

LINE 2
(a) world beyond my own
(b) clubs not usually shown
(c) people I could bone

LINE 3
(a) talked to a real person
(b) left my room
(c) seen a living being

LINE 4
(a) got this goddamn phone
(b) live in my parents' home
(c) have no car I own

My _____
1

the _____.
2

I haven't _____
3

since I _____.
4

FREE VERSE

LINE 1
ⓐ bends in the wind
ⓑ grows tall when mowers protest
ⓒ makes me itch

LINE 2
ⓐ kites act as weather vanes
ⓑ lovers make plans they'll never enact
ⓒ hucksters play three-card monte

LINE 3
ⓐ give voice to joyous spring
ⓑ steal the last popsicle
ⓒ squeal like feral cats

LINE 4
ⓐ hark
ⓑ dude
ⓒ WTF

LINE 5
ⓐ meteorologist calls for thunderstorms
ⓑ hot dog vendor has no gluten-free buns
ⓒ meter maid just gave me a ticket

Grass _____ .
                          1

Vivacious _____ .
                              2

Children _____ .
                            3

But _____ ,
                      4

the _____ .
                     5

LINE 1

ⓐ I fell for that Nigerian scam
ⓑ Waze me from this traffic jam
ⓒ Wham-bam, thank you, ma'am

I do not like green eggs and ham.

_____

1

LINE 1
ⓐ Desire
ⓑ Your dad bod
ⓒ Sucking face

LINE 2
ⓐ just between you and me
ⓑ something and nothing too
ⓒ not what I expected

LINE 3
ⓐ or don't
ⓑ gently
ⓒ right now

_____ is cool.
                1

That's _____.
                2

So love me _____.
                3

LINE 1
ⓐ Meet me at the local bar
ⓑ Hands caught in the cookie jar
ⓒ Scoring chicks with a guitar

Twinkle, twinkle, little star,

_____!

RHYMED VERSE

LINE 1
ⓐ narrow crevice
ⓑ shaded glen
ⓒ jagged outcrop

LINE 2
ⓐ radiant light fails to reach
ⓑ harsh gales blow from the beach
ⓒ echoes the hunting hawk's screech

LINE 3
ⓐ jackrabbit questions
ⓑ cougar asks a bear to explain
ⓒ lemur does a dance about

LINE 4
ⓐ taste of a peach
ⓑ skills that it can teach
ⓒ morals of a leech

In a _____
1

where _____,
2

a _____
3

the _____.
4

IN THE STYLE OF WILLIAM CARLOS WILLIAMS

LINE 1
ⓐ inhaled
ⓑ stolen
ⓒ regurgitated

LINE 2
ⓐ artisanal pickles
ⓑ frozen hot pockets
ⓒ donuts Bob bought for the team

LINE 3
ⓐ that were
ⓑ you tried to hide
ⓒ that sat tauntingly

LINE 4
ⓐ plain sight
ⓑ your desk drawer
ⓒ the office fridge

LINE 5
ⓐ probs
ⓑ like, totally
ⓒ obvs

LINE 6
ⓐ the afternoon slump
ⓑ another sad lunch in the
    break room
ⓒ no good reason

LINE 7
ⓐ Excuse
ⓑ Hold
ⓒ Don't rat on

LINE 8
ⓐ yummy
ⓑ unlabeled
ⓒ not really yours anyway

LINE 9
ⓐ salty
ⓑ tempting
ⓒ lovely

LINE 10
ⓐ seductive
ⓑ shiny
ⓒ perfect and eff you

"This Is Just to Say"

I have _____
1

the _____
2

_____ in
3

_____
4

and which

you were _____
5

saving

for _____
6

_____ me
7

they were _____
8

so _____
9

and so _____
10

SHAKESPEAREAN SONNET

LINE 1
ⓐ do spit into our wine
ⓑ cut in this checkout line
ⓒ commit another crime

LINE 2
ⓐ brought some queso dip please stay
ⓑ hate the game let players play
ⓒ came in April leave in May

LINE 3
ⓐ air fresheners smell of pine
ⓑ photos of our ex, the swine
ⓒ kids out back making green slime

LINE 4
ⓐ returns their lunch tray
ⓑ spits, but your speech sprays
ⓒ sleeps less than all day

LINE 5
ⓐ wheels my chair further from my youth
ⓑ cares not when chickens come
   to roost
ⓒ has passed since sitting in this booth

LINE 6
ⓐ band at last will take the stage
ⓑ wheezing grunts of grandpa's rage
ⓒ show gets much better with age

LINE 7
ⓐ vanishes with a loud "ka-poof"
ⓑ finds my bare bottom so uncouth
ⓒ makes drinks with too much
   damn vermouth

LINE 8
ⓐ fire scorched the room like
   Jimmy Page
ⓑ reeks of patchouli and of sage
ⓒ cleaner works for a living wage

LINE 9
ⓐ sound like quite a bore
ⓑ hurt hammies we tore
ⓒ get us out of chores

LINE 10
ⓐ stop making rude armpit sounds
ⓑ forget that porkpie hat I found
ⓒ tell what happened at the
   campground

LINE 11
ⓐ back issues of Fantastic Four
ⓑ mixers I'll make a drink to pour
ⓒ pics I'll mock you for what you wore

LINE 12
ⓐ is here, so let's go downtown
ⓑ rages until the lunch bell sounds
ⓒ remains, Almond Joy or Mounds

LINE 13
ⓐ the ungodly hour of the night
ⓑ my inability to fight
ⓒ the fact that my pants are too tight

LINE 14
ⓐ probably smell rather ripe
ⓑ find I scratch and sometimes bite
ⓒ poop his shorts and need to wipe

Before the Fates _____
1

Let all who _____
2

And find our _____.
3

Neither king nor fool _____.
4

Though time _____,
5

We hear the _____.
6

The moon _____.
7

My hearth _____.
8

For though our end may _____,
9

I will ne'er _____
10

with these _____.
11

The battle _____.
12

Despite _____,
13

Know Death will _____.
14

SURREALIST

LINE 1
ⓐ lunch counter
ⓑ row of cubicles
ⓒ foldout couch

LINE 2
ⓐ reeks of marmalade
ⓑ holds no kettle-cooked potato chips
ⓒ offers lots of canned tuna

LINE 3
ⓐ airport bar
ⓑ yellow brick road
ⓒ line at the ATM

LINE 4
ⓐ my imaginary friend
ⓑ the murderous cyborg from the future
ⓒ Pete

LINE 5
ⓐ a taco truck
ⓑ Amarillo, Texas
ⓒ my vacant soul

Across the vast _____ ,
                                1

my cupboard _____ .
                                2

Along the _____ ,
                                3

the footsteps of _____
                                4

_____

lead to _____ .
                                5

LINE 1
ⓐ Anxiety
ⓑ Ol' Saggy Bits
ⓒ Tequila Shots

LINE 2
ⓐ bubble burster
ⓑ vanity cure
ⓒ for shame spirals

LINE 3
ⓐ Blah blah blah poor
ⓑ Oy! Stop judging
ⓒ Big whatevs from

Dear _____:
                         1

Perfect _____, yay!
                         2

_____ me.
                         3

LINE 1

ⓐ poop on the lawn of this mansion

ⓑ lick this mystery substance on
the sidewalk

ⓒ pose for your #dogsofinstagram pic

LINE 2

ⓐ chow time

ⓑ a rendezvous with the bitch
next door

ⓒ sniffing butts

LINE 3

ⓐ keeper of the kibble

ⓑ holder of the dreaded leash

ⓒ my indentured man-slave

LINE 4

ⓐ endless love and devotion

ⓑ a pat on the head and a bowl of
crunchy bits

ⓒ a lot of pointing and demands

LINE 5

ⓐ bark every time someone walks by the
house

ⓑ limit indoor peeing to thrice weekly

ⓒ do whatever I want anyway

LINE 6

ⓐ the two-legged gods watch over
and keep you

ⓑ our mutually beneficial symbiosis
continue late into your human years

ⓒ you never realize the deep animosity
I feel toward you but am afraid
to show

"Ode to the Master from His Four-Legged Friend"

As I _____ ,
1

I look forward to _____
2

Knowing that you, _____ ,
3

Will provide me with _____
4

_____ .

In return, I promise to _____
5

_____ .

May _____
6

_____ !

LINE 1
ⓐ I don't buy Jack's stupid schtick
ⓑ Jack be chef will make you sick
ⓒ Jack run if the charges stick

Jack be nimble, Jack be quick,

1.

LIMERICK

LINE 1
ⓐ with a gun in his hand
ⓑ in a cool klezmer band
ⓒ who was Army command

LINE 2
ⓐ shoot at a distant eland
ⓑ travel to a distant land
ⓒ eat only tuna that's canned

LINE 3
ⓐ a humongous sneeze
ⓑ a recent deep freeze
ⓒ a big hunk of cheese

LINE 4
ⓐ shoot his own knees
ⓑ need some more Z's
ⓒ Mad Cow Diseased

LINE 5
ⓐ the rest of his life he can't stand
ⓑ his legs were quite cold but
not tanned
ⓒ his regiment now sits unmanned

A man _____
1

had to _____.
2

Yet _____
3

made him _____
4

so _____.
5

FREE VERSE

LINE 1
ⓐ four fresh baguettes and Swiss cheese
ⓑ a baby unicorn
ⓒ her ex-boyfriend's iPhone

LINE 2
ⓐ whips and you watch her nae nae
ⓑ is overconditioned
ⓒ looks like a helmet

LINE 3
ⓐ an aluminum steed
ⓑ a wheeled broom
ⓒ without brakes

LINE 4
ⓐ nuns
ⓑ confused pigeons
ⓒ Sailor Moon cosplayers

The basket on her bicycle holds _____
                                          1

_____ .

Her burnished hair _____ ,
                                    2

piloting _____
                 3

around a crowd of _____ .
                          4

LINE 1
ⓐ feed the soul
ⓑ are so hard
ⓒ might seem cool

LINE 2
ⓐ when hungry
ⓑ when dating
ⓒ for class nerds

LINE 3
ⓐ Don't count on it
ⓑ But not really
ⓒ Can't stop wedgies

Poems _____1_____.

Especially _____2_____.

_____3_____ though.

FREE VERSE

LINE 1
ⓐ that one tall dude
ⓑ a billboard
ⓒ garbage

LINE 2
ⓐ pays no mind
ⓑ lights up the sky like a sun
   or something
ⓒ is seriously super hot

LINE 3
ⓐ a smoke break
ⓑ a meme
ⓒ my deodorant

LINE 4
ⓐ time takes time
ⓑ of a kidney stone hurts
ⓒ lane is full of idiots

LINE 5
ⓐ wake up wondering where we are
ⓑ make it to the state line
ⓒ find my car keys

Hidden by _____,
                            1
the sun _____.
                       2
As fleeting as _____,
                           3
the passing _____
                        4
until we _____.
                     5

LIMERICK

LINE 1
ⓐ the weird looks I may get
ⓑ my unusual pet
ⓒ my sad life of regret

LINE 2
ⓐ put on my head a baguette
ⓑ carry a butterfly net
ⓒ play this antique clarinet

LINE 3
ⓐ big as a bear
ⓑ incredibly rare
ⓒ odor is fair

LINE 4
ⓐ has plenty of wear
ⓑ tastes like an éclair
ⓒ will make people swear

LINE 5
ⓐ I want fame on the internet
ⓑ it's clear that I've lost a bad bet
ⓒ I'll just tell folks I'm Boba Fett

Despite _____ 1 ,

I'll _____ 2 .

It's _____ 3

and _____ 4 .

But _____ 5 .

RHYMED VERSE

LINE 1
ⓐ a tiny lad
ⓑ a wee bit sad
ⓒ a teenaged cad

LINE 2
ⓐ a guru in a van
ⓑ a circus caravan
ⓒ a real-life Peter Pan

LINE 3
ⓐ told me drugs are rad
ⓑ messed me up so bad
ⓒ looked so very mad

LINE 4
ⓐ go real crazy, man
ⓑ happily lesbian
ⓒ dance the cancan

When I was _____
1

I met _____,
2

who _____.
3

It made me _____.
4

FREE VERSE

LINE 1
ⓐ pies on the windowsill
ⓑ the locker room
ⓒ butts

LINE 2
ⓐ survive the breeze
ⓑ escape my brain
ⓒ penetrate the void

LINE 3
ⓐ repeatedly sneeze
ⓑ lie down and have a nap
ⓒ barf

LINE 4
ⓐ my self-esteem
ⓑ a place to eat
ⓒ Jimmy Hoffa

LINE 5
ⓐ promise I'll start my diet tomorrow
ⓑ hit the snooze button
ⓒ play that Katy Perry song

LINE 6
ⓐ advantage of my sick day
ⓑ extra Taco Bell hot sauce packets
ⓒ some time off for good behavior

The echo of _____
1

struggles to _____.
2

It beckons me to _____
3

and find _____.
4

Again and again I _____,
5

taking _____.
6

FREE VERSE

LINE 1
(a) wilts
(b) attracts bees
(c) was delivered to the wrong person

LINE 2
(a) some sticky notes
(b) my flask of rye
(c) a plate of crab wontons

LINE 3
(a) clown shoes
(b) chaps and nothing else
(c) Disney-princess gowns

LINE 4
(a) mock me
(b) hold up the ceiling pretty well
(c) clash with my yellow tie

LINE 5
(a) talk about *Game of Thrones* by the watercooler
(b) order from that awful Thai place again
(c) steal pens from the supply room

➤ On the desk a bouquet _____
1

_____.

It sits next to _____.
2

Men walk by clad in _____.
3

Gray walls seem to _____
4

while we _____.
5

LINE 1
ⓐ is wondrous
ⓑ is a bitch
ⓒ means baseball

LINE 2
ⓐ drop off branches and die
ⓑ require much raking
ⓒ me couch-bound drinking beers

LINE 3
ⓐ thank the gods!
ⓑ move southward
ⓒ gain ten pounds

Winter _____.
1

Leaves _____.
2

I shall _____.
3

FREE VERSE

LINE 1
(a) arms stretch wide to grip the wheel
(b) clothing smells of stale cigarettes and pasteurized cheese
(c) life goes toot toot, beep beep

LINE 2
(a) eat sandwiches on white bread every day
(b) sure do miss the good ol' days
(c) take pills to both sleep and wake up

LINE 3
(a) deliver your child door to door
(b) obey every traffic law
(c) have eyes in the back of my head

LINE 4
(a) this job will be done by robots
(b) I'll show them all
(c) I will be 65 and cash right the bleep out

LINE 5
(a) keep on truckin'
(b) hit the gas and go anyway
(c) go home and have a beer

My _____ 1 _____

_____.

I _____ 2 _____.

You trust me to _____ 3 _____.

Someday _____ 4 _____.

But for now I'll _____ 5 _____.

ODE

LINE 1
(a) a hot blast of emotion from the very furnace of my heart
(b) a box of chocolates, you never know what you're gonna get
(c) the rutting season of the mighty elk, which comes but once a year and is conducted against a tree

LINE 2
(a) azure oceans into which I see infinity
(b) two huge bowls of vanilla pudding with raisins in the center
(c) two deep puddles I'm extra careful not to step in

LINE 3
(a) supple and fruity, like the finest wine
(b) real sugary, like iced cake flowers
(c) slightly salty, like sliced deli meat

LINE 4
(a) creamy smooth, scented sweetly of rose petals
(b) shiny and slippery, smelling like tropical banana sunscreen
(c) rough and worn in patches, like the quilt draped on my grandma's couch

LINE 5
(a) a perfect pear
(b) a pale harvest moon
(c) so squeezable

LINE 6
(a) the sun, the moon, and the stars
(b) across town, just not at rush hour
(c) into the back seat

LINE 7
(a) be mine forever
(b) be with me tonight
(c) be less picky and swipe right for once

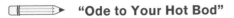 **"Ode to Your Hot Bod"**

My love for you is like _____
                                          1

_____.

Your eyes are like _____
                                      2

_____.

Your lips are _____.
                                3

Your skin is _____
                              4

_____.

And your butt is like _____.
                                    5

To be with you I would move _____
                                                6

_____.

Please my love, will you _____
                                        7

_____?

FREE VERSE

LINE 1
ⓐ glorious cake
ⓑ late-night binge watching
ⓒ stinky socks

LINE 2
ⓐ ones who skip work
ⓑ lady who dances badly
ⓒ bananas

LINE 3
ⓐ mascots remove their stuffed heads
ⓑ the hot tub gets cold
ⓒ our best intentions are to do the worst

LINE 4
ⓐ band plays Beyoncé
ⓑ ants invade the picnic of life
ⓒ marchers march in March

LINE 5
ⓐ fills with hot air balloons
ⓑ looks a tad overcast
ⓒ cries Mary

LINE 6
ⓐ Chuck E. Cheese tokens
ⓑ more homework
ⓒ some really sick skate moves

A song of _____
　　　　　　　　　　　1

exalts the _____.
　　　　　　　　　　2

For when _____,
　　　　　　　　　3

the marching _____
　　　　　　　　　　4

and the sky _____,
　　　　　　　　　5

regaling the children with _____.
　　　　　　　　　　　　　　　　6

LIMERICK

LINE 1
ⓐ lopsided cat
ⓑ vampire bat
ⓒ housefly or gnat

LINE 2
ⓐ avoid all the rats
ⓑ look out for some hats
ⓒ check this way and that

LINE 3
ⓐ starts to run
ⓑ sees the sun
ⓒ bites someone

LINE 4
ⓐ not be much fun
ⓑ become undone
ⓒ cost you a ton

LINE 5
ⓐ end up going splat
ⓑ be seen as a brat
ⓒ get into a spat

When walking your _____,
                        1

it's best to _____.
                    2

For if it _____,
                  3

things will _____
                   4

and you'll likely _____.
                        5

LINE 1
ⓐ be praised
ⓑ time suck
ⓒ porn site

LINE 2
ⓐ the world be as one
ⓑ my click finger strong
ⓒ Russian trolls happy

LINE 3
ⓐ Bots are the
ⓑ Doomed is the
ⓒ #winning the

Internet _____!

　　　　　　　　　1

You make _____.

　　　　　　　　　2

_____ future.

　　　　　　　3

FREE VERSE

LINE 1
ⓐ Fat gold watches
ⓑ Beef tacos
ⓒ Rainbows and lollipops

LINE 2
ⓐ naked mind
ⓑ secret fantasies
ⓒ sweat-lodge hallucinations

LINE 3
ⓐ the darkness dawning in my soul
ⓑ letters floating in my alphabet soup
ⓒ the best dystopian YA novel ever

LINE 4
ⓐ mud
ⓑ beneath the rock under which I long
   to hide
ⓒ H-E double hockey sticks

LINE 5
ⓐ that same drawing I've been drawing
   since I was a kid, a lone walrus under
   a palm tree on a tiny island
ⓑ my bow back fiercely, like Katniss
   from *The Hunger Games*
ⓒ upon my existential angst

LINE 6
ⓐ it had all been a dream
ⓑ my math teacher's calling on me
ⓒ I shouldn't drink coffee before bed

_____ swirl

1

in my _____

2

like _____.

3

Peering up from _____,

4

I draw _____

5

_____

and realize _____.

6

LINE 1
ⓐ beautiful
ⓑ totes bunk, man
ⓒ to ponder

LINE 2
ⓐ a box of puppies
ⓑ me out of my funk
ⓒ crayons to draw with

LINE 3
ⓐ sense matters not
ⓑ things get hairy
ⓒ the booze runs out

Life is _____.
                              1

Bringing _____,
                              2

when _____.
                              3

"Poetry, the best words in the best order." –Samuel Taylor Coleridge

Created, published, and distributed by Knock Knock
1635 Electric Ave.
Venice, CA 90291
knockknockstuff.com
Knock Knock is a registered trademark of Knock Knock LLC

ISBN: 978-168349085-2
UPC: 825703-20005-8

10 9 8 7 6 5 4 3 2 1